A play by Bob W

TRICKY
BISCUITS

Illustrations by Garry Parsons

Characters

Miss Bell

Miss Bell is not very good at guessing what the biscuits mean.

Milly

Milly tries to be funny and interrupts a lot.

Akbar

Akbar finishes the play with the funniest joke!

William

William is calm
and sensible.

Katie

Katie gives clever answers.

Josh

Josh is keen to be
liked by his teacher.

TRICKY BISCUITS

Miss Bell Today we're going to make gingerbread biscuits.

All Hooray!

Katie I want to mix the ingredients.

Akbar Can I roll out the dough?

William Cutting the dough into a biscuit shape is the best bit.

Josh I love the smell when they're cooking!

Milly The best bit's at the end – eating them!

Miss Bell Here are the ingredients. There's flour, sugar, golden syrup, milk, eggs, butter, and, of course, ginger.

Milly Yummy!

Miss Bell Now, can anybody tell me what we're going to do now?

Milly Eat them.

Miss Bell Don't be silly, Milly.

Katie I know, Miss!

Miss Bell Yes, Katie?

Katie We're going to measure them out into a bowl and then mix them together to make a dough.

Miss Bell That's right. Then what shall we do with the dough mixture?

Milly Eat it.

Miss Bell You're being silly again, Milly.

Akbar I know, Miss!

Miss Bell Yes, Akbar?

Akbar We roll it flat with a rolling pin.

Miss Bell That's right, Akbar. Very good. What next?

Milly I know, Miss!

William I know, Miss!

Miss Bell Yes, William?

William We cut the dough into a special shape. Last time we made gingerbread men.

Milly Miss!

Josh And then we put them in the oven until they're golden.

Milly Miss! Miss!

Miss Bell Yes, Milly. What is it?

Milly You know when I've measured out my ingredients and mixed them up into dough?

Miss Bell Yes.

Milly And when I've rolled the dough flat with a rolling pin?

Miss Bell Yes.

Milly And when I've cut the dough into the shape of a gingerbread man and cooked him? Can I bite his head off?

Miss Bell No.

Milly   Why not?

Miss Bell   Because there's a parents' evening at school tonight. The biscuits are for your mums and dads to eat when they have their cup of tea. I want you to make a biscuit into a shape that has something to do with your mum or dad.

Josh   I don't understand. What do you mean, Miss?

Miss Bell   Well, if your dad's hobby is fishing you could make him a biscuit in the shape of a fish.

Josh   Oh, I see. My mum likes gardening, so I could make her a biscuit in the shape of a flower.

Miss Bell   Yes, you've got the right idea, Josh.

Akbar   Please, Miss. My mum and dad haven't got time for hobbies. They're always too busy working.

Miss Bell   Then you could cut your biscuit into a shape that had something to do with your mum or dad's work. What they make, for example.

Akbar   What do you mean?

Josh   I know! If your dad is a builder your biscuit could look like a house.

Miss Bell   That's right, Josh.

Akbar   You want me to make my biscuit into the shape of what my dad makes?

Miss Bell   Yes.

Akbar   That's easy, Miss.

Miss Bell   Good. Okay, everyone. Let's get to work.

Later ...

Miss Bell Now that all the biscuits are cooked, let's have a look at the shapes you've made. Your biscuit is square, William.

William Yes, Miss. Shall I tell you what it is?

Miss Bell No, let us guess.

Katie Is it a window? Your dad must be a window cleaner.

William No. It's to do with his hobby.

Katie Does he use something square for his hobby?

William Yes. His hobby is watching the telly.

Miss Bell   Oh, I see. Now, Josh. Your biscuit is shaped like a bird.

Josh   Yes, Miss. Shall I tell you why?

Miss Bell   No, let us guess.

William   Is your dad's hobby birdwatching?

Josh   No. It's to do with my mum's job. And it's not meant to be just any bird. It's an owl.

Akbar   Your mum works with owls?

Josh   No, but you have to be like an owl to do my mum's job.

12

William I don't understand. Does she work at night?

Josh No. Shall I tell you what she does? She's a teacher.

Miss Bell Why is a teacher like an owl?

Josh Because owls are very wise.

Miss Bell Oh, yes, I see. That's very good, Josh. I like that.

Josh (*to Milly*) I thought she would.

Miss Bell Now, Milly. Is your biscuit meant to be a hat?

Milly Yes, Miss. Shall I tell you why?

Miss Bell No. Let us guess.

Katie Does your Mum work in a hat shop?

Milly No. It's for my Dad. And it's not to do with his job. It's to do with his hobby.

William His hobby?

Milly Yes. It's not just any hat. It's a top hat. Like the one he wears in front of the bathroom mirror.

Miss Bell I don't understand, Milly.

Milly My dad's hobby is magic. He spends his spare time learning how to do magic tricks. That's why I had to make two biscuits.

Miss Bell You made two biscuits?

Milly Yes. I made one biscuit in the shape of a top hat and another one in the shape of a rabbit. Then I put the rabbit biscuit under the top hat biscuit and waved a pencil over them and the rabbit biscuit disappeared!

Akbar That's amazing!

Katie Wow!

William You made the rabbit biscuit disappear?

Josh How did you do that?

Milly I ate it!

Miss Bell Milly?

Milly Yes, Miss?

Miss Bell You're very silly. Now, Katie. Is this your biscuit?

15

Katie Can you tell what it's meant to be, Miss? It's for my mum. It's a tap. You know, like a bath tap.

Miss Bell Well, in that case I guess your mum must be a plumber.

Katie No, it's not to do with her job. It's to do with her hobby.

Akbar Her hobby?

Katie She does it to keep fit, two nights a week at the leisure centre.

Miss Bell I don't understand.

Katie Shall I tell you what she does, Miss? She goes to dancing classes. She's learning how to tap dance.

Miss Bell Katie?

Katie Yes?

Miss Bell You're even sillier than Milly. I hope you've not been silly, Akbar.

Akbar No, Miss. I've done exactly what you told me to do. Shall I tell you what it's meant to be?

Miss Bell No. Let us guess. Hmm. It's in the shape of a circle. So maybe it's meant to be a wheel.

Akbar No, Miss. It's not a wheel.

Miss Bell Is it a dinner plate?

Akbar No.

Josh A saucer?

Akbar No.

Katie A ball?

Akbar No.

William A dustbin lid?

Akbar No.

Milly The sun?

Akbar No.

Miss Bell A flying saucer?

Akbar Now **you're** being silly, Miss. Shall I tell you what it is?

Miss Bell Yes.

Akbar It's a biscuit.

Miss Bell I can see it's a biscuit, Akbar! I want to know what it's meant to look like.

Akbar It's meant to look like a biscuit. You told me to cut my biscuit into the shape of the things my dad makes when he's at work. So I did.

Miss Bell I don't understand.

Akbar My dad's a baker, Miss. Shall I tell you what he bakes?

Miss Bell No. Don't tell me. I think I can guess. He makes ...

Everyone Biscuits!

READY, STEADY, ACT!

Now that you have read this play it's time to act it out. You will tell your audience the story using words, actions and maybe some costumes and props.

CHOOSING THE PARTS

Choose who will play each part.

- Miss Bell is the teacher. She is not very good at guessing what the biscuits mean.
- Milly tries to be funny and interrupts a lot.
- Katie gives clever answers.
- Akbar finishes the play with the funniest joke!
- William is calm and sensible.
- Josh is keen to be liked by his teacher.

Who in your cast would be best at these roles? Read a few lines of the play to test this out. Miss Bell has lots of lines so choose carefully. Make name stickers for your characters to wear.

> ### Did you know ...?
> Weird biscuit shapes have included a complete 32-piece edible chess set.

SETTING THE SCENE

Be sure to let your audience know where you are and how the characters are feeling as soon as you start.

Have you ever cooked in school? Is there a special place or do you use your usual classroom? Do you have special equipment, like sieves and measuring cups? Talk about baking something delicious. What kind of preparation does the teacher have to do?

Sit in a circle and take turns at coming into the middle and miming something that you would do in a kitchen. People in the circle can guess what you are doing. You might:

- butter some bread
- wash up
- toss a pancake
- crack and peel a hard-boiled egg.

WHAT YOU WILL NEED

Costumes

Dressing up can help you to pretend to be another character. Think about Miss Bell. How will you make her look like a grown-up? Will you give everyone an apron? How will you make them? Could you use big sheets of paper? Could you decorate them?

Remember that your actors don't have to look exactly like the pictures in the book. Draw the characters.

Props

Read through the play and decide what props you will need. Empty food containers will do for the ingredients. You will need some bowls, spoons and baking trays. You will need a rolling pin but use it carefully. Make the biscuits from paper or salt dough.

Did you know ...?
... How to make salt dough? 1 cup of flour, 1 cup of salt and half a cup of water. Knead them together until they are smooth and springy. Use it for making models.

SPEAKING AND MOVING

Speaking

Practise saying, 'Hooray!' and 'Biscuits!' altogether. Let all the actors say their first line using a different emotion. Maybe Akbar is excited, Josh is hungry and Milly likes to be funny. Choose the best ideas to help the audience get to know the characters.

Moving

Practise moving to the front when it's your turn to talk to Miss Bell.

There are some actions – mixing, rolling, shaping and putting trays into an oven – that you will need to mime.

How will you show the audience that time has passed while the biscuits have been in the oven cooking? One idea might be to make the sound of a kitchen timer. Or the ticking of a clock.

What next?

When you have performed this play, you might want to:

- put in an extra scene while the biscuits are in the oven
- make some biscuits.